THE BOOSEY & HAWI SONG COLLECTION VOL 2

• *1901–2004* •

selected by Eileen Field

BOOSEY & HAWKES

Boosey & Hawkes Music Publishers Ltd
www.boosey.com

Published by Boosey & Hawkes Music Publishers Ltd
Aldwych House
71–91 Aldwych
London
WC2B 4HN

www.boosey.com

ISMN M-060-11624-7
ISBN 0-85162-472-3

First impression 2005

Printed in England by Halstan & Co Ltd, Amersham, Bucks

Music origination by Point Note, France

CONTENTS

Preface

It has been my pleasure, yet again, to spend time in the basement of Boosey & Hawkes Music Publishers when located in London's Regent Street. From the wealth of music housed in the archive, I have been able to choose a further selection of songs, ranging in difficulty from moderately easy to more advanced. To these are added a number of previously unpublished songs and others specially composed for this second volume. As in the first, I have attempted to produce a balanced, attractive and interesting selection, with songs whose vocal ranges are not excessive, making them accessible to singers of all ages and experience. The performance notes at the back of the book provide a snapshot of each song and a starting point from which the singer and accompanist can develop their own interpretation.

Eileen Field

Préface

C'est avec un plaisir renouvelé que, dans les sous-sols de Boosey & Hawkes Music Publishers alors sur Regent Street à Londres, j'ai pris le temps de rassembler, à partir de la richesse du fond de musique conservé dans les archives, une nouvelle sélection d'airs à chanter de niveau moyen à avancé, à laquelle s'ajoutent un certain nombre de pièces vocales encore inédites et d'autres composées spécialement pour ce deuxième volume. Comme dans le premier volume, je me suis efforcée de proposer un choix équilibré et attrayant d'œuvres présentant toutes un intérêt et dont les tessitures vocales ne soient pas excessives de manière à être accessibles aux chanteurs de tous âges et possédant des expériences différentes. Les remarques sur l'interprétation situées en fin de volume fourniront un aperçu de chaque air et un point d'appui sur lequel le chanteur et son accompagnateur pourront élaborer leur propre interprétation.

Eileen Field
Traduction : Agnès Ausseur

Vorwort

Es ist mir nun zum wiederholten Male vergönnt gewesen, einige Zeit im Keller des Musikverlags Boosey & Hawkes in der Londoner Regent Street zu verbringen. Aus der Fülle der im dortigen Archiv enthaltenen Musik konnte ich eine weitere Auswahl von Liedern zusammenstellen, deren Schwierigkeitsgrad vom gemäßigt leichten bis zum fortgeschrittenen Stück reicht. Hinzu kommen einige bislang unveröffentlichte Lieder und weitere, die speziell für diesen zweiten Band komponiert wurden. Wie beim ersten Band habe ich mich bemüht, eine ausgewogene, ansprechende und interessante Auswahl vorzulegen, mit Liedern, deren Stimmumfang nicht übermäßig groß ist, so dass sie Sängerinnen und Sängern aller Altersgruppen und jeglichen Erfahrungsgrads zugänglich sind. Die Anmerkungen zur Aufführungspraxis am Schluss des Hefts liefern einen ersten Eindruck von jedem Lied und einen Ausgangspunkt, von dem aus Sängerinnen, Sänger und Begleiter ihre eigene Interpretation entwickeln können.

Eileen Field
Übersetzung: Bernd Müller

The swing

Words by
ROBERT LOUIS STEVENSON

Music by
LIZA LEHMANN

The sky above the roof

English words by
MABEL DEARMER
from PAUL VERLAINE

Music by
RALPH VAUGHAN WILLIAMS

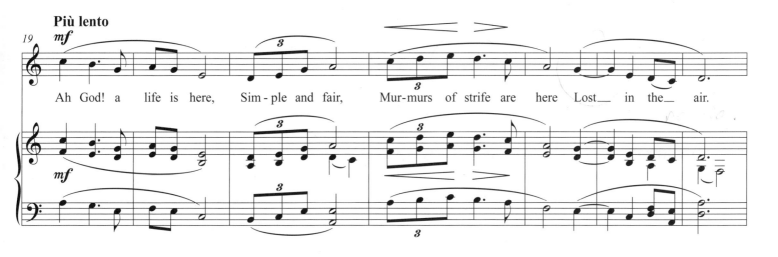

Più lento

Ah God! a life is here, Sim - ple and fair, Mur-murs of strife are here Lost__ in the__ air.

Why dost thou weep, O heart, Poured out in tears? What hast thou

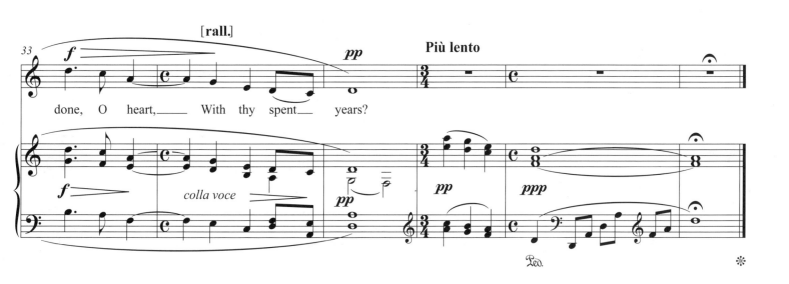

done, O heart,____ With thy spent____ years?

colla voce

O mistress mine

Words by
WILLIAM SHAKESPEARE

Music by
ROGER QUILTER

poco rit.   a tempo

end in lov - ers' meet - ing, Ev' - ry wise man's son doth know.___

poco rit.   a tempo

What is love? 'tis not here -

- af - ter; Pre - sent mirth hath pre - sent laugh - ter; What's to come is still un -

8

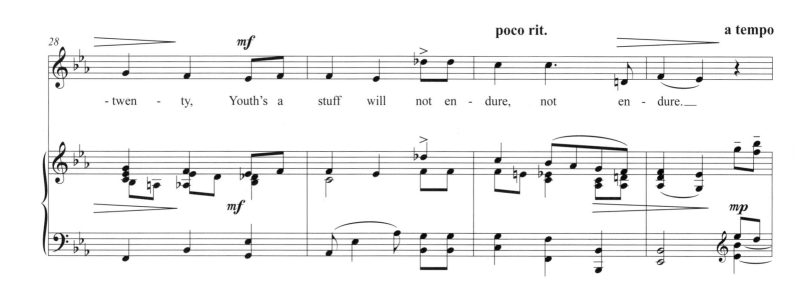

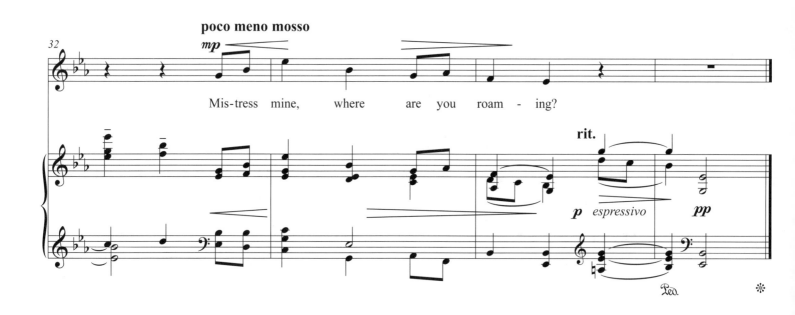

She moved thro' the fair

Words adapted from
an old ballad by
PADRAIC COLUM

Music: Traditional air
from County Donegal
arr. HERBERT HUGHES

My___ young love said to me___ "My__ mo-ther won't mind And my fa-ther___ ___ won't slight you for your lack of kind,"___ And she stepp'd___ a-way

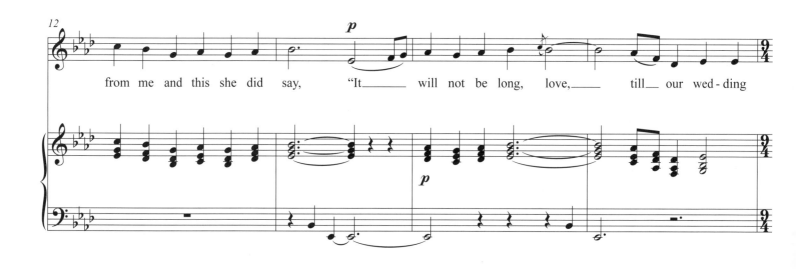

from me and this she did say, "It___ will not be long, love,___ till__ our wed - ding

day." She___ stepp'd a - way from me___

___ and she went thro' the fair, And__ fond - ly___ I watch'd her move here and move

there,_____ And___ then she_____ went home - ward with one star a - wake, As the___

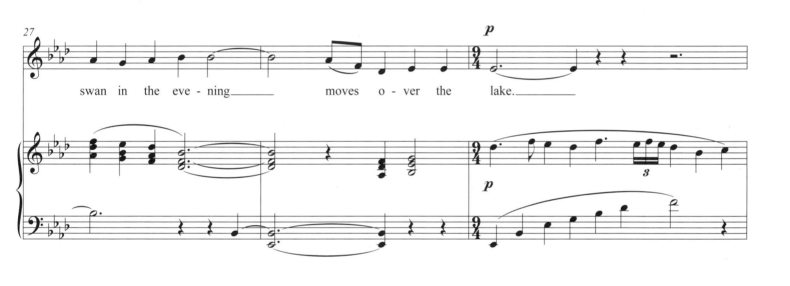

swan in the eve - ning_____ moves o - ver the lake._____

Last___ night she came to me,_____ she___ came soft - ly

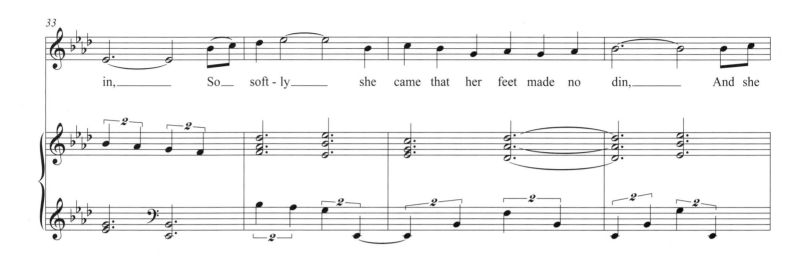

in,_____ So__ soft - ly_____ she came that her feet made no din,_____ And she

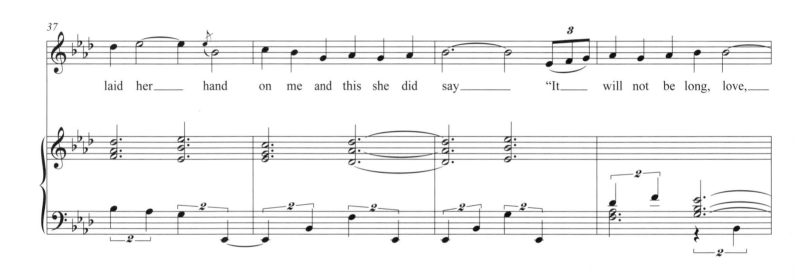

laid her_____ hand on me and this she did say_____ "It_____ will not be long, love,

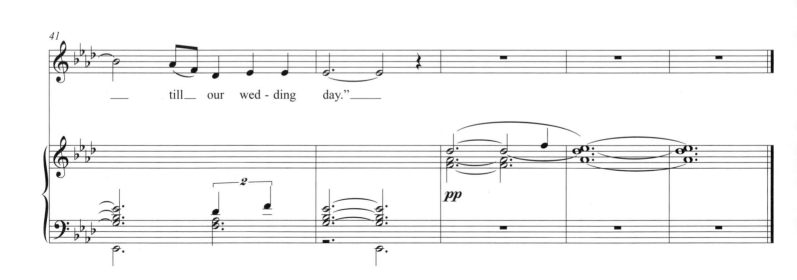

___ till__ our wed - ding day."_____

To Mrs Edmund Fisher

Linden Lea

A Dorset Song

Words by
WILLIAM BARNES

Music by
RALPH VAUGHAN WILLIAMS

With - in the
(Original) *'Ith - in the*

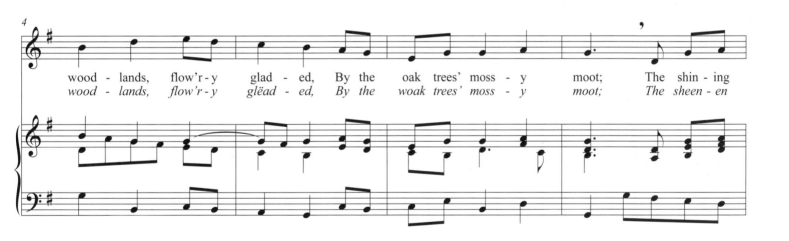

wood - lands, flow'r - y glad - ed, By the oak trees' moss - y moot; The shin - ing
wood - lands, flow'r - y glëad - ed, By the woak trees' moss - y moot; The sheen - en

grass blades, tim - ber sha - ded, Now do qui - ver un - der foot; And birds do
grass blëades, tim - ber shëad - ed, Now do qui - ver un - der voot; An' birds do

© Copyright 1912 by Boosey & Co. Ltd

14

28
sing - ing, Up up - on the tim - ber tops; And brown leaved fruit's a - turn - ing
zing - en, Up up - on the tim - ber tops; An' brown leaved fruit's a - turn - ing

32
red, In cloud - less sun - shine o - ver - head, With fruit for me, the ap - ple
red, In cloud - less zun - sheen au - ver - head, Wi' fruit vor me, the ap - ple

36
tree Do lean down low in Lin - den Lea.
tree Do lean down low in Lin - den Lea.

colla voce

mp

Animato

f

rit.

40
Let o - ther folk make mo - ney fas - ter; In the
Let o - ther vo'k mëake mo - ney vas - ter; In the

f

E'en as a lovely flower

Words by
KATE KROEKER
after HEINRICH HEINE

Music by
FRANK BRIDGE

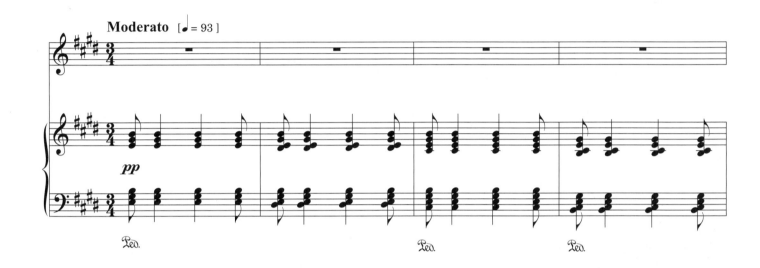

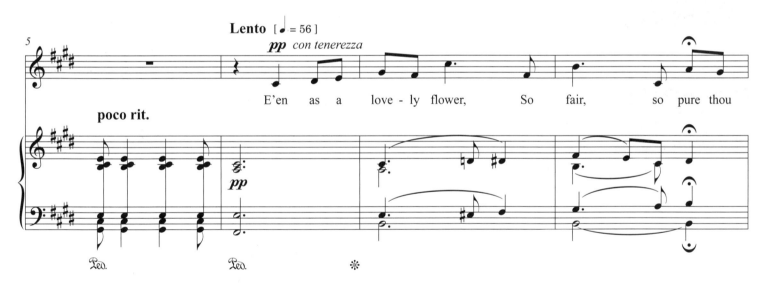

E'en as a love-ly flower, So fair, so pure thou

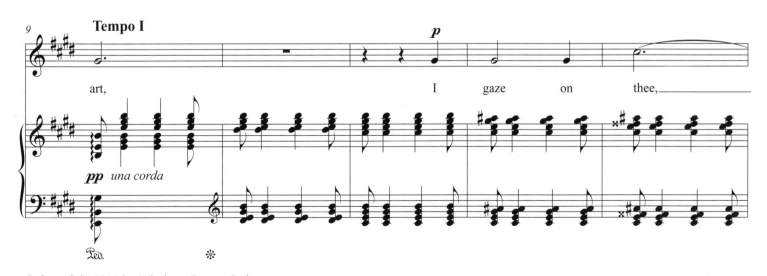

art, I gaze on thee,_____

and sad - - - ness Comes steal - - ing, comes

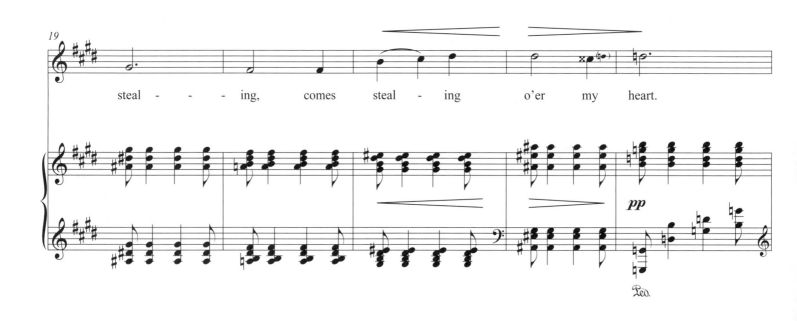

steal - - ing, comes steal - ing o'er my heart.

My hands I fain had

fold - - -ed Up - on___ thy soft brown hair,

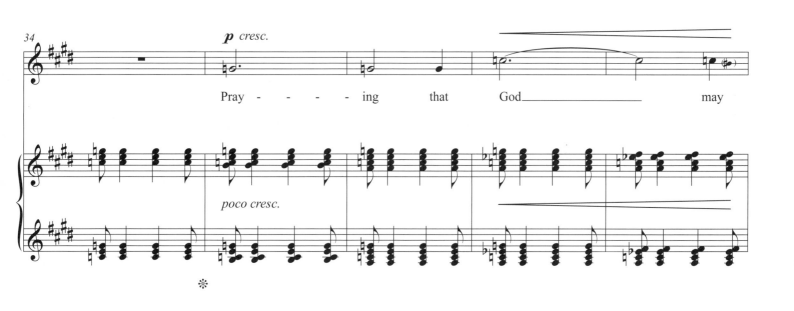

Pray - - - ing that God___ may

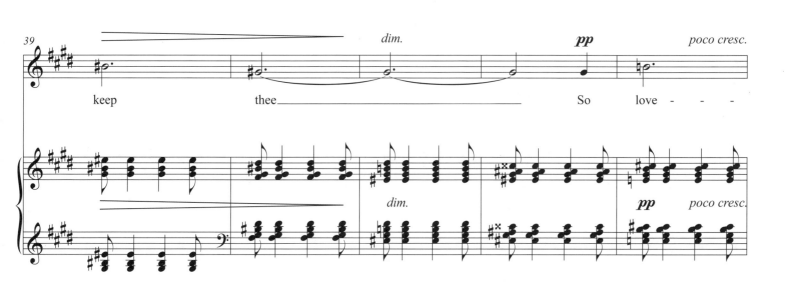

keep thee___ So love - - -

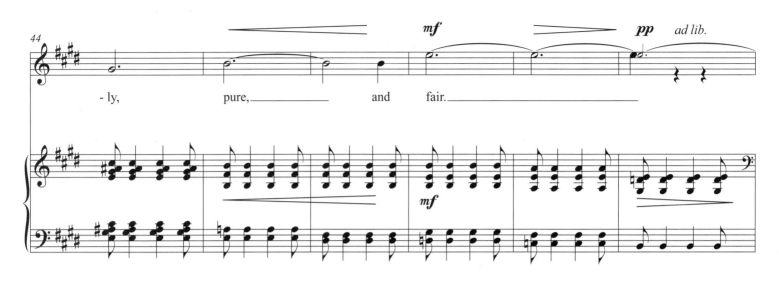

- ly,   pure,_____ and fair._____

E'en   as   a   love - ly flower,   so

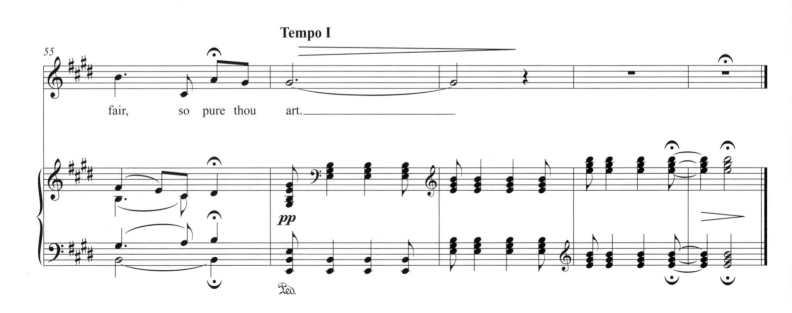

fair,   so   pure thou   art._____

Spring sorrow

Words by
RUPERT BROOKE

Music by
JOHN IRELAND

Poco andante [♩ = c.72]

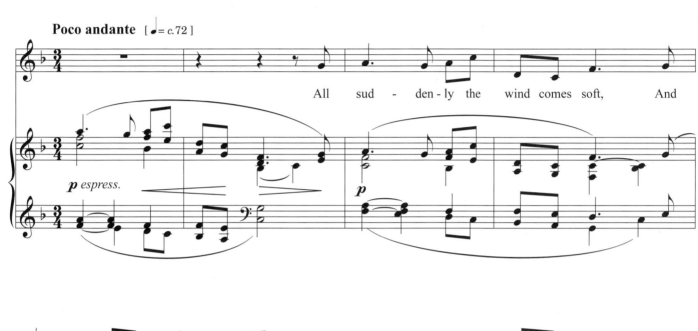

All sud - den - ly the wind comes soft, And

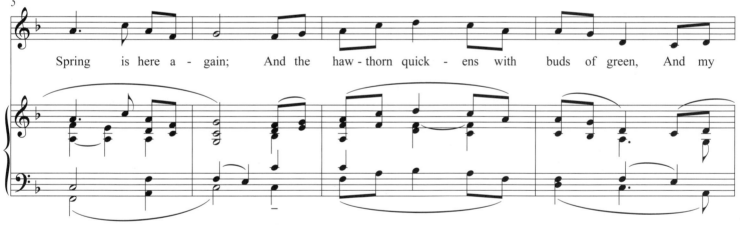

Spring is here a - gain; And the haw - thorn quick - ens with buds of green, And my

heart with buds of pain. My_ heart all Win - ter lay so numb, The

This poem is reprinted from *1914 and other Poems* by Rupert Brooke, by permission of the Literary Executor and Messers Sidgwick and Jackson Ltd

earth so dead and frore, That I nev - er thought__ the Spring would come, Or my

heart wake a - ny more. But Win - ter's brok - en and earth has

wok - en, And the small birds cry a - gain; And the haw - thorn hedge__ puts

forth its buds And my heart puts forth its pain.__

I have twelve oxen

Words:
EARLY ENGLISH

Music by
JOHN IRELAND

Allegretto grazioso [♩ = c. 100]

I have twelve ox - en that be fair and brown, And they go a - graz - ing down by the town. With hey!_ with ho! with hey!_____ with ho! Saw - est not you mine ox - en, you

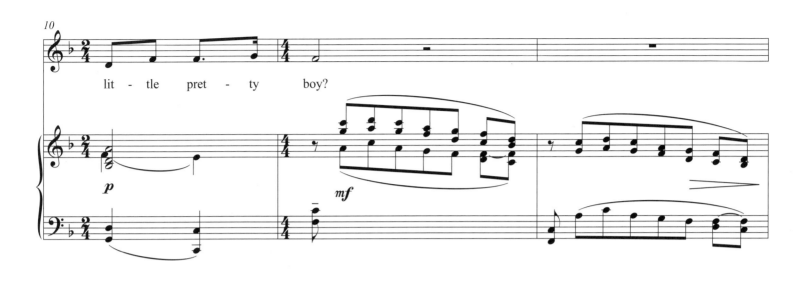

lit - tle pret - ty boy?

I have twelve ox - en, they be fair and white, And they go a - graz - ing

down by the dyke. With hey!_ with ho! with hey!_____ with ho! Saw - est

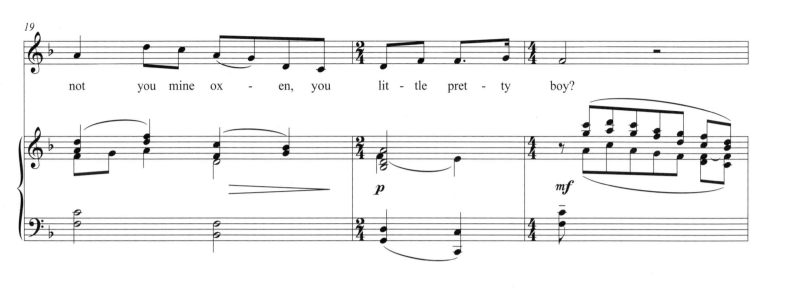

not you mine ox - en, you lit - tle pret - ty boy?

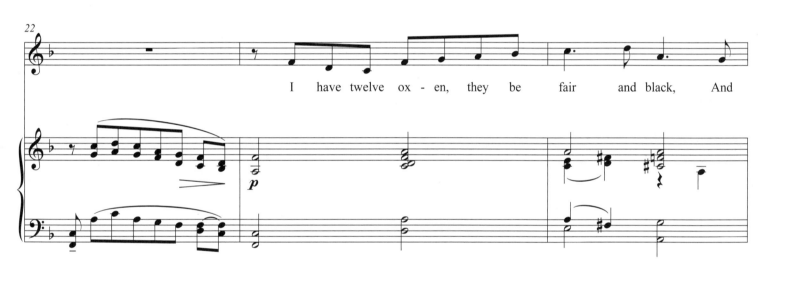

I have twelve ox - en, they be fair and black, And

they go a - graz - ing down by the lake. With hey!__ with ho! with

hey!_____ with ho! Saw - est not you mine ox - en, you lit - tle pret - ty

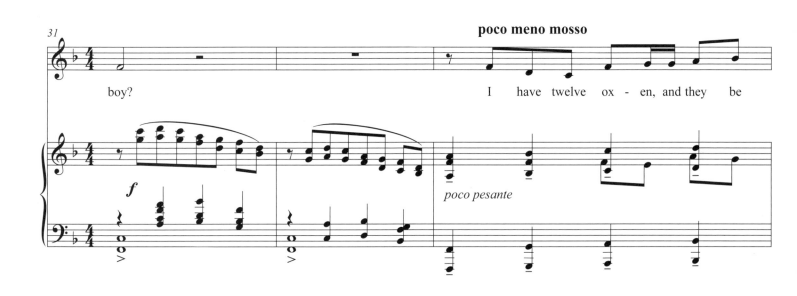

poco meno mosso

boy? I have twelve ox - en, and they be

fair and red, And they go a - graz - ing down_ by the mead. With

The ships of Arcady

Words by
FRANCIS LEDWIDGE

Music by
MICHAEL HEAD

Moderato *(not too slow)* [♩ = 72]

Thro' the faint-est fi-li-gree___ O - ver the dim___ wa-ters go___

Lit-tle ships of Ar-ca-dy___ When the morn-ing moon is low___

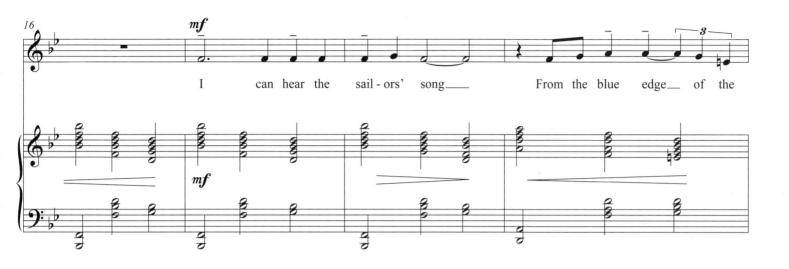

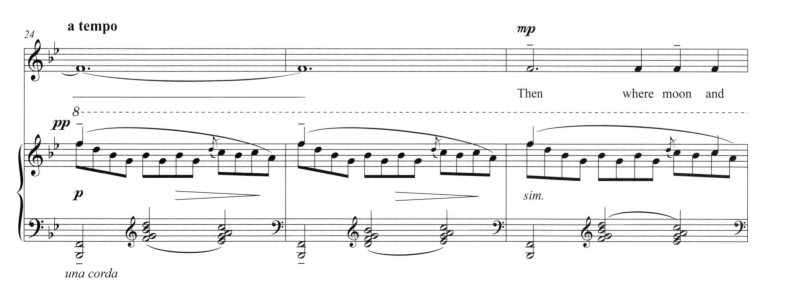

waters meet   Sail____ by sail they pass a - way,   With

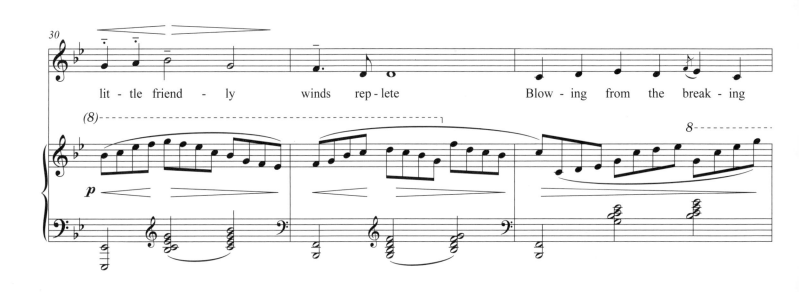

lit - tle friend - ly winds rep - lete   Blow - ing from the break - ing

day._____   And when the lit - tle ships have flown,

tre corde

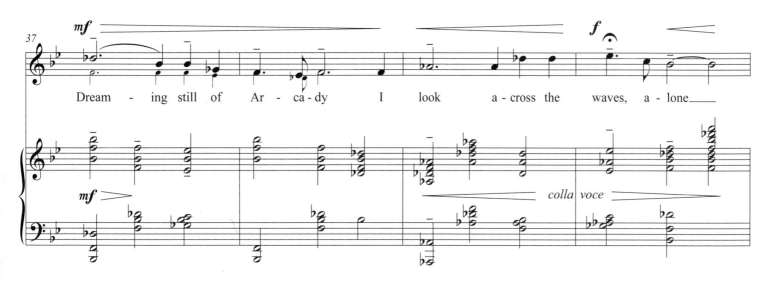

Dream - ing still of Ar - ca - dy I look a - cross the waves, a - lone

In the mis - ty fi - li - gree.

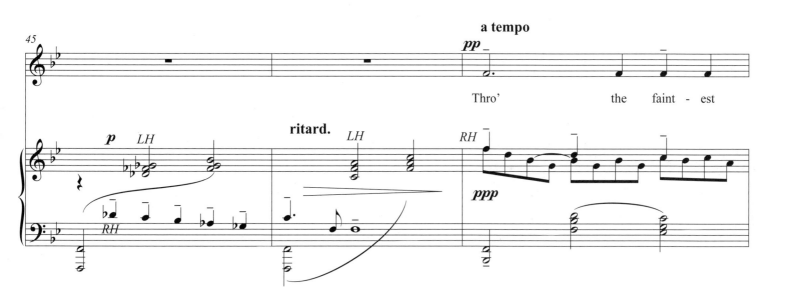

Thro' the faint - est

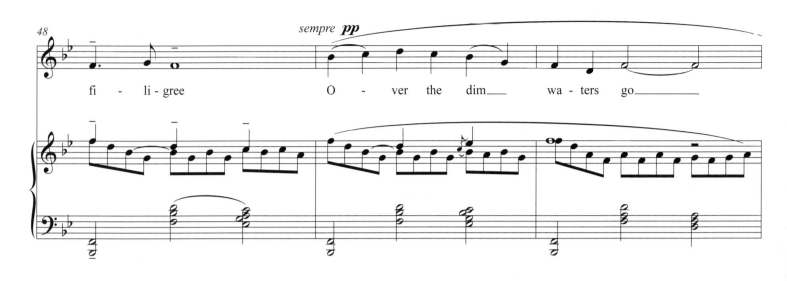

fi - li - gree   O - ver the dim___ wa - ters go___

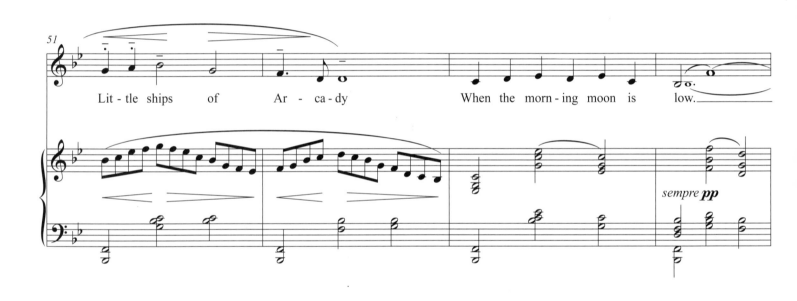

Lit - tle ships   of   Ar - ca - dy   When the morn - ing moon is   low.___

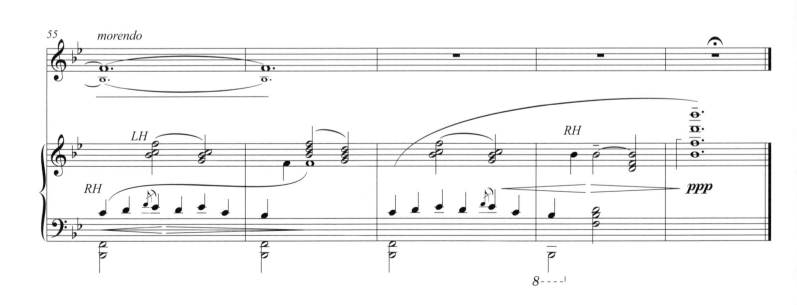

Trade winds

Words by
JOHN MASEFIELD

Music by
FREDERICK KEEL

With a smooth flowing rhythm [♩ = c.116–120]

In the har-bour, in the is-land, in the

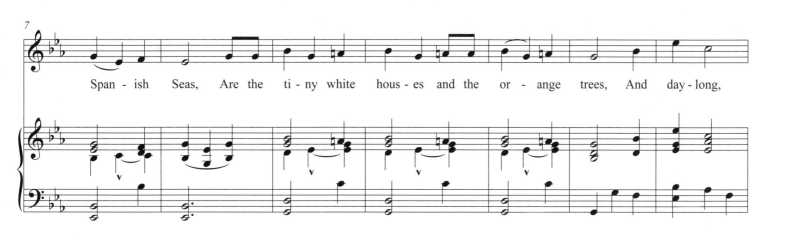

Span-ish Seas, Are the ti-ny white hous-es and the or-ange trees, And day-long,

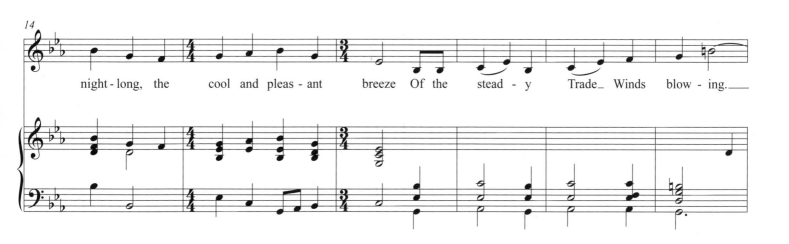

night-long, the cool and pleas-ant breeze Of the stead-y Trade_ Winds blow-ing._

The widow bird

Words by
PERCY BYSSHE SHELLEY

Music by
HERBERT HOWELLS

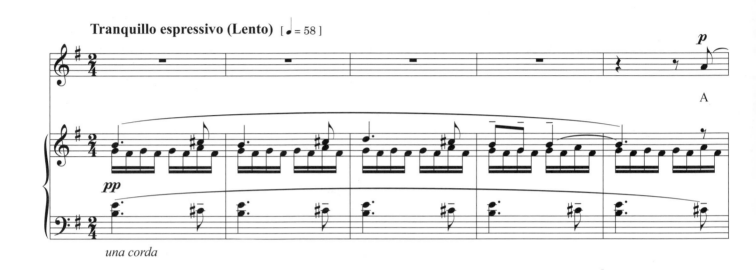

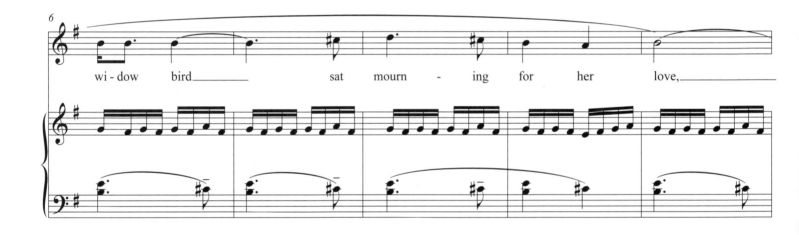

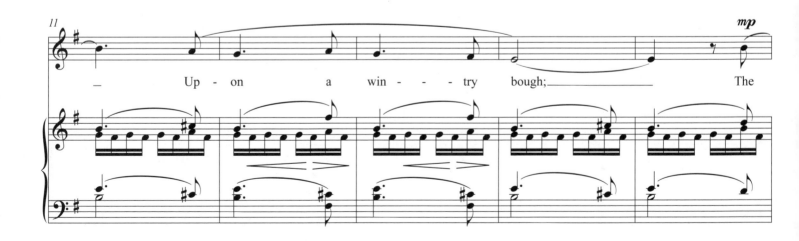

froz - - en wind crept on a - bove,____

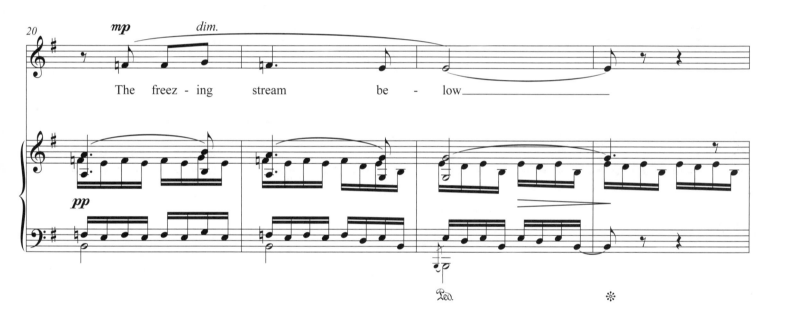

The freez - ing stream be - low____

There was no leaf up - on the

for - - est bare_____ No flower_____ up - on the

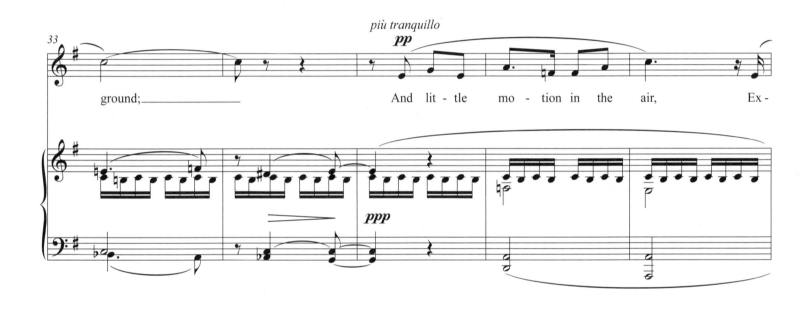

ground;_____ And lit - tle mo - tion in the air, Ex -

- cept the mill - - - - wheel's sound._____

Infant Joy

Words by
WILLIAM BLAKE

Music by
REBECCA CLARKE

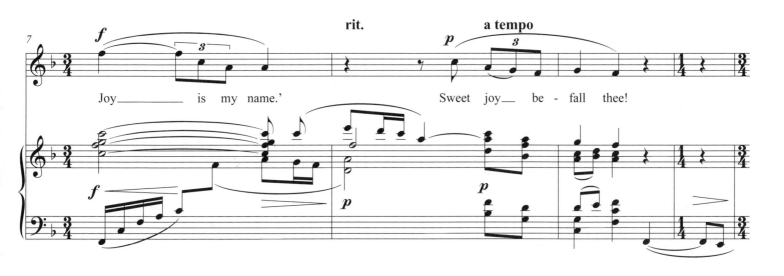

A little slower

Pret - ty Joy! Sweet joy, but two__ days old. Sweet____

Gradually back to Tempo I

____ joy I call thee: Thou__ dost smile, I

sing____ the while, Sweet joy__ be - fall____ thee!

To Marjorie

Sweet Suffolk owl

Words by
THOMAS VAUTOR

Music by
ELIZABETH POSTON

Sweet Suf - folk Owl, So trim - - - ly dight_____ With

42

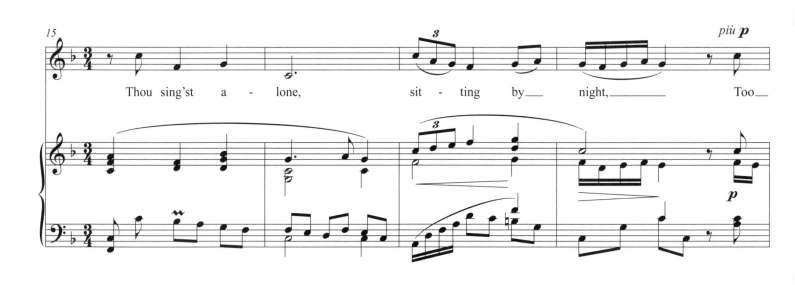

whoo!

Thy note,_____ that forth_ so free - ly_ rolls, With shrill_____

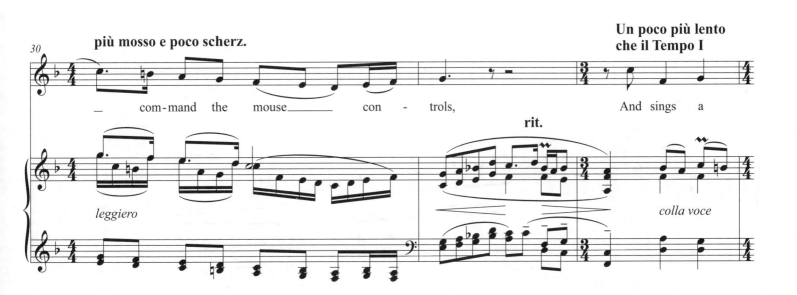

_ com-mand the mouse_____ con - trols, And sings a

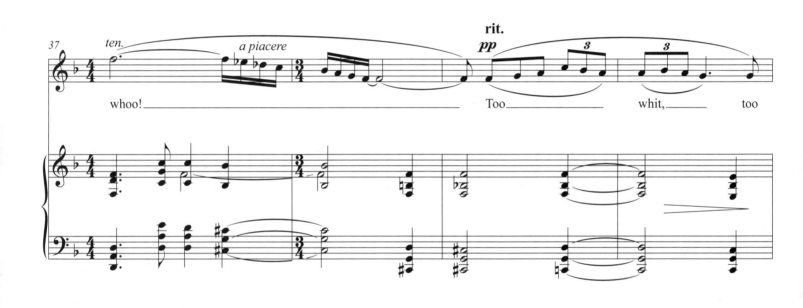

For my mother

The birds

Words by
HILAIRE BELLOC

Music by
BENJAMIN BRITTEN

When Je - sus Christ was four years old, The
an - gels brought Him toys of gold, Which no man e - ver had bought or sold.
And yet with these___ He

would not play. He made Him small fowl out__ of clay, And

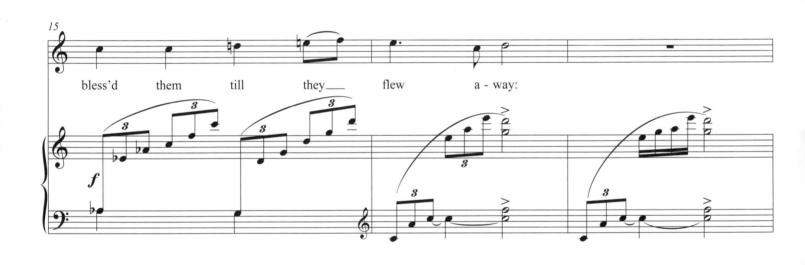

bless'd them till they__ flew a - way:

Animato

Tu cre - as - ti, Do - mi - ne.

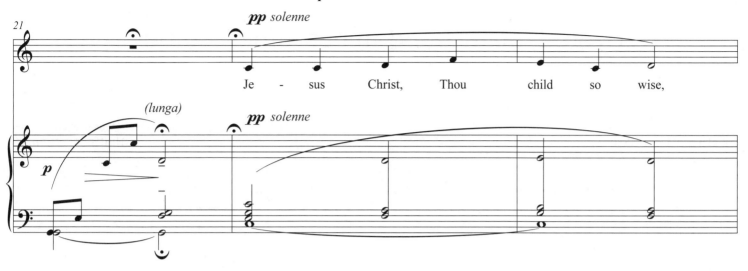

Je - sus Christ, Thou child so wise,

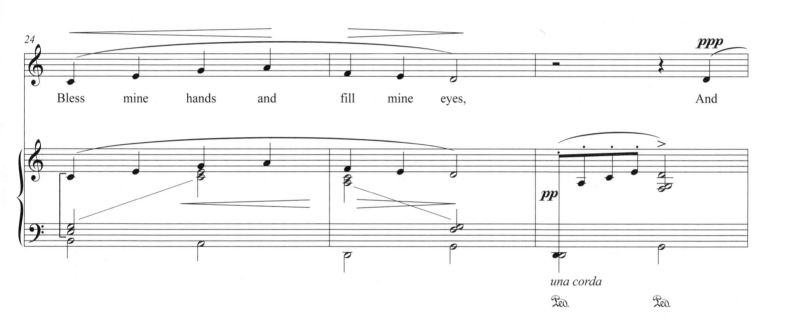

Bless mine hands and fill mine eyes, And

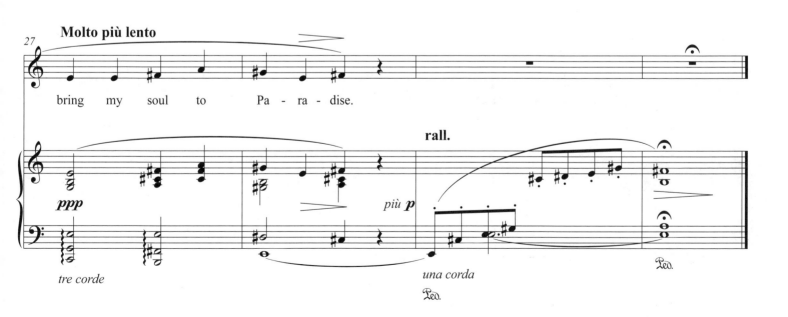

bring my soul to Pa - ra - dise.

A young maid stood in her father's garden

Words:
TRADITIONAL IRISH

Music arranged by
HERBERT HUGHES

A young maid stood in her fa-ther's gar-den, Pluck-ing ro-ses all co-ver'd with dew; A stran-ger came and gazed up-on her And said "Fair la-dy, will you wed with me?" "It's se-ven years since I had a

50

hands they were slim and__ small, And up be - tween them he pulled a gold__ ring, And when she

saw it she down did fall. He took her up and gave her sweet kiss - es And he em -

- braced her so ten - der - ly Say-ing, "I am your true and_ lov - ing sai - lor That came from

sea for to wed with you."_____

Mamble

Words by
JOHN DRINKWATER

Music by
MICHAEL HEAD

might be a Mam - ble bro - ken That was lis - som in a dream. So

leave the road to Mam - ble And take a - no - ther road To as good a place as Mam - ble Be it

la - zy as a toad; Who trav - els Wor - cester coun - ty Takes a - ny place that comes When

★ The song may end here   ⊕ The bars between these signs may be omitted

O your eyes are dark and beautiful

English words by
PETER CARROLL

Music by
MÁTYÁS SEIBER

O your eyes_ are_ dark and beau-ti-ful, Glow-ing, spark-ling_ dark and beau-ti-ful,

Sun-kiss'd o - lives_ warm and_ sweet, Sun- kiss'd o - lives_ warm and_ sweet.__

Soft - ly in_ my_ heart, my dar - ling, I shall hear_ it_ till I_ die,

I shall hear_ it_ till I_ die.

I shall_ hear_ it_ till I_ die, I shall_ hear_ it_ till I_ die.

To Nell Tangeman

Little elegy

Words by
ELINOR WYLIE

Music by
NED ROREM

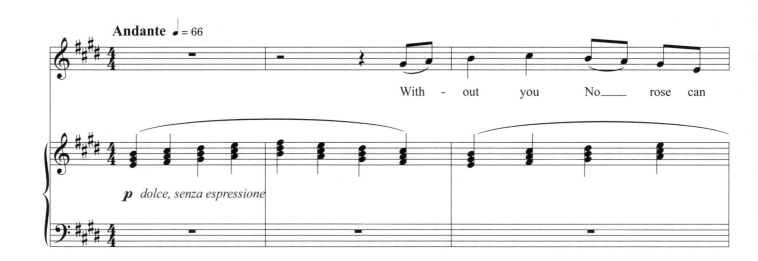

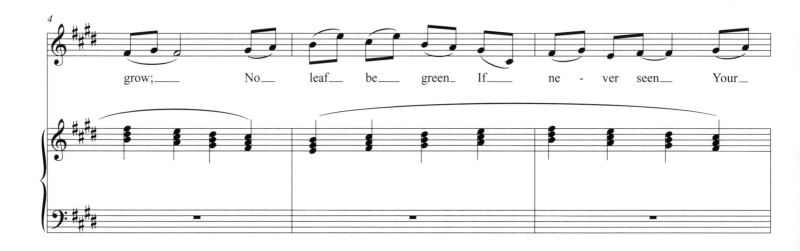

From *Two Songs* © copyright 1952 by Boosey & Hawkes Inc

New York City, 28 March 1948

(Spring, cool, bright, noon)

See, see, mine own sweet jewel

Words:
ANON. ?16th century

Music by
MICHAEL ROSE

Long time ago

Ballad
adapted by GEORGE POPE MORRIS

Music arranged by
AARON COPLAND

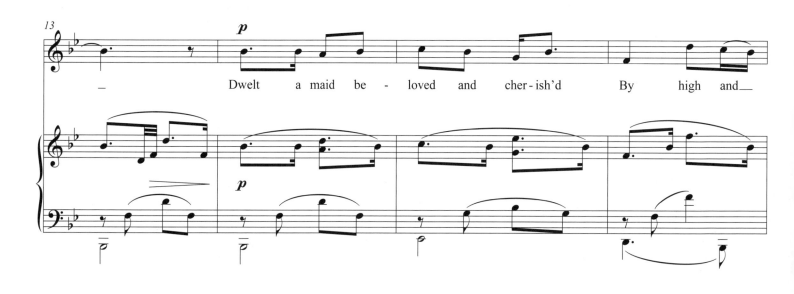

Dwelt a maid be - loved and cher - ish'd By high and

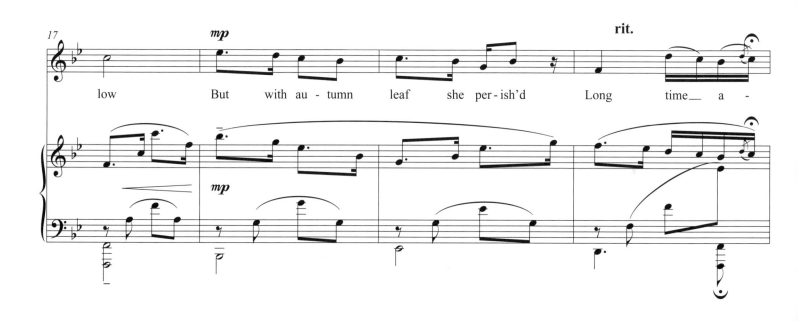

low But with au - tumn leaf she per - ish'd Long time a -

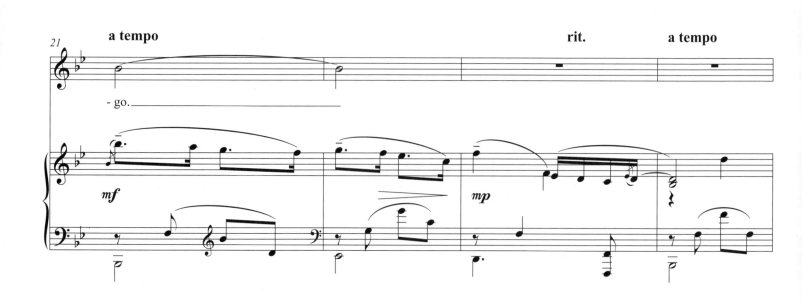

- go.

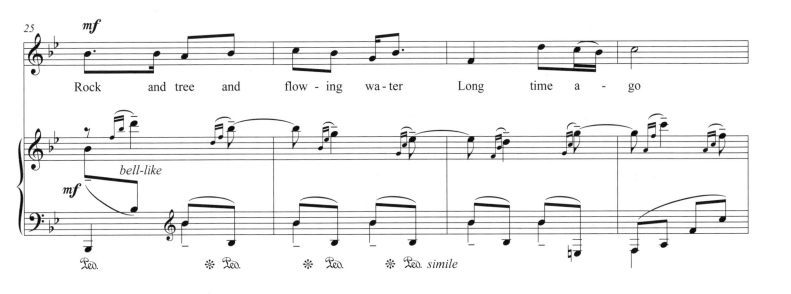

low Ten - der - ly her blue eyes glis - ten'd

Long time a - - go.

To Daniel Pinkham

On a singing girl

Words by
ELINOR WYLIE

Music by
NED ROREM

sud - den Night:
On your light limbs,
O

love-li - est,
May the dust be light!

The little horses

Music adapted by
AARON COPLAND

LULLABY

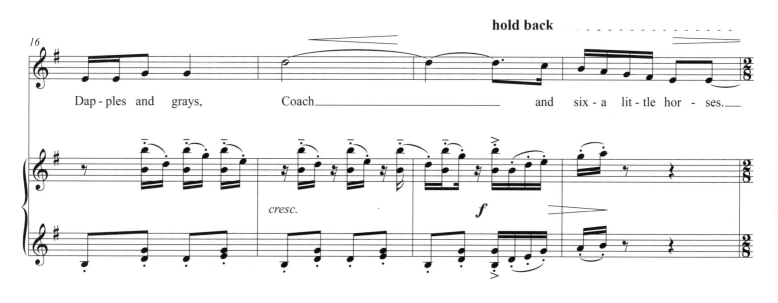

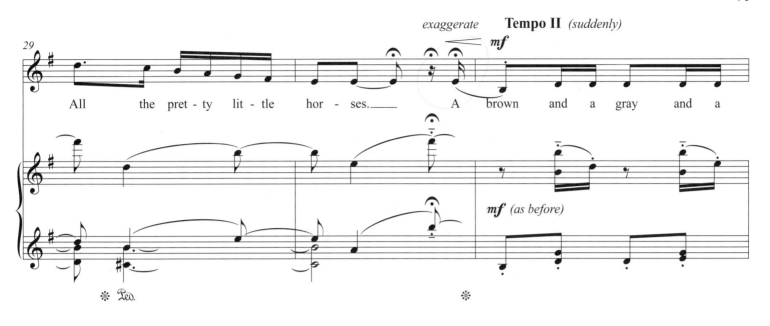

All the pret - ty lit - tle hor - ses. ___ A brown and a gray and a

black and a bay and a Coach and six - a lit - tle hor - ses. A

black and a bay and a brown and a gray and a Coach ___

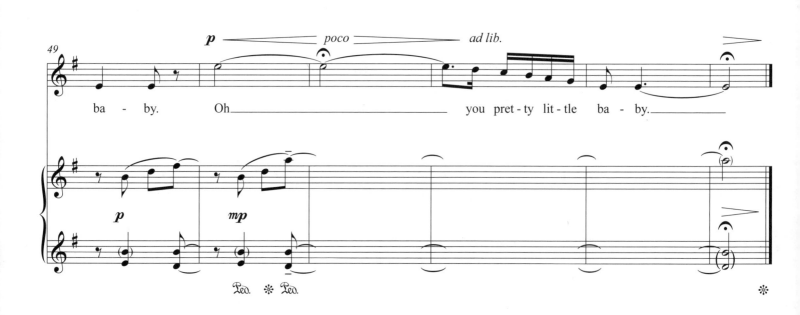

For Susan

The lark in the clear air

Words by
SAMUEL FERGUSON

Music: Traditional Irish air
arranged by MICHAEL ROSE

Dear__ thoughts are in__ my__ mind, And my__ soul__ soars en-

-chan - ted As I hear the sweet__ lark__ sing, in the__ clear air of the day. For a

ten - der bea - ming__ smile To my hope__ has__ been__ grant - ed, and to-

-mor - row she __ shall __ hear All my __ fond __ heart would say. I shall tell her all __ my __

love, All my heart's __ a - dor - a - tion, And I think __ she __ will __ hear __ And

will not say me __ nay. It is this that gives __ my __ heart All its joy - ous e -

- la - tion, As I hear that sweet __ lark __ sing in the __ clear __ air of the day.

The apron of flowers

Music arranged by
HOWARD FERGUSON

IRISH FOLKSONG

★ All grace-notes before the beat.   A few suggested alterations in the words have been added in square brackets

76

In praise of ale

Words:
ANON. 16th CENTURY

Music by
ROBERT DRAY

Bring us in good ale. Bring us in no mut-ton, sirs, for that is ve-ry lean, and

Bring us in no trypes, sir, for they be sel-dom clene, but Bring us in good ale,__ sirs,__

bring us in good ale, And for our dear La-dy-love, Bring us in good ale.

Bring us in no pork, sirs, for that is ve - ry fat, and bring us in no wheat - en bread, for

nei - ther love I that, but Bring us in good ale,— sirs,— Bring us in good ale.

And for our dear La - dy - love, Bring us in good ale. Bring us in no veal, sirs, that

82

do I not de-sire, But bring us in good ale e-nough to drink__ by the fire,__

Bring us in good ale,__ sirs,__ Bring us in good ale, And for our dear La-dy-love,

Bring us in good ale._____

The Virgin's cradle hymn

Words copied from an old print by
SAMUEL TAYLOR COLERIDGE

Music by
ROBERT DRAY

Si_ non dor - mis, Ma - ter plo - rat, in - ter fi - la can - tans_ or - at,

in - ter fi - la can - tans or - at._____ Blan - de ve - ni,

blan - de ve - ni, som - nu - le, som - nu - le._____

Spell of creation

Words by
KATHLEEN RAINE

Music by
CHRISTOPHER FIELD

Lyrics:
With-in the flower there lies a seed, In the seed there springs a tree, In the tree there spreads a wood.

In the wood there burns a fire, And in the fire there melts a stone, With-in the stone a ring of iron.

With-in the ring there lies an O, In the O there looks an eye, In the

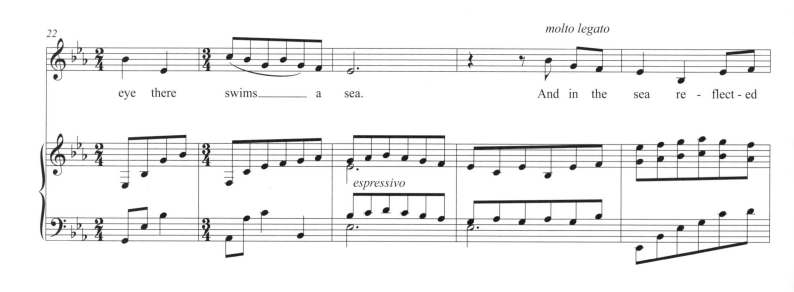

eye there swims____ a sea. And in the sea re-flect-ed

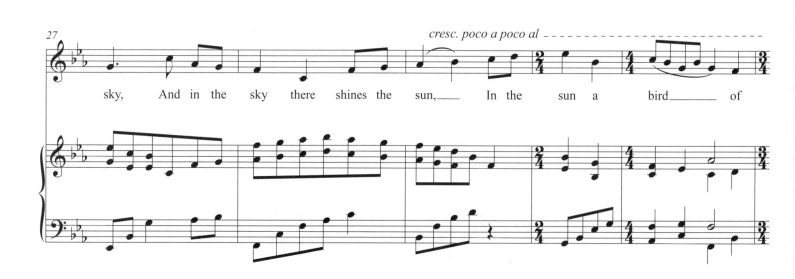

sky, And in the sky there shines the sun,____ In the sun a bird____ of

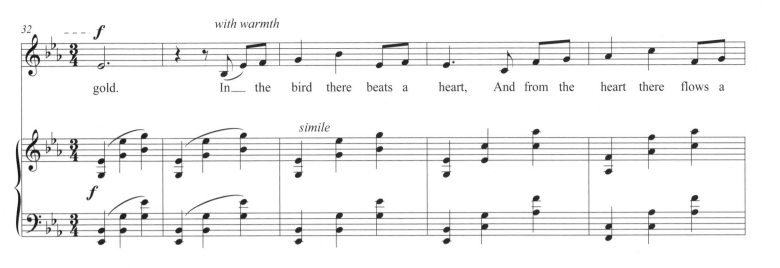

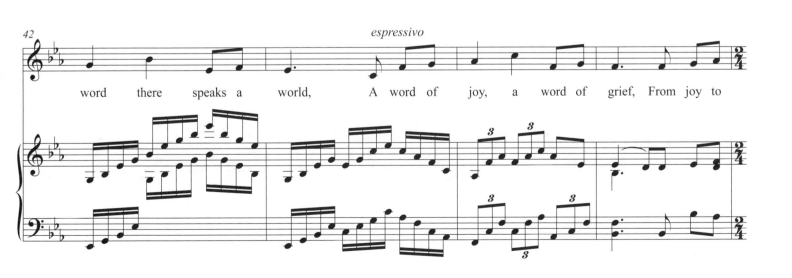

grief there springs_____ my love. Oh love, my

love, there springs a world, And on the world there shines a sun,_____ And in the

sun there burns_____ a fire. In_____ the

fire con - sumes my heart, And in my heart there beats a bird, And in the

dim. poco a poco al - - - -

bird there wakes an eye, With - in the eye, earth, sea and

Simply, as at first

molto legato   *simile*

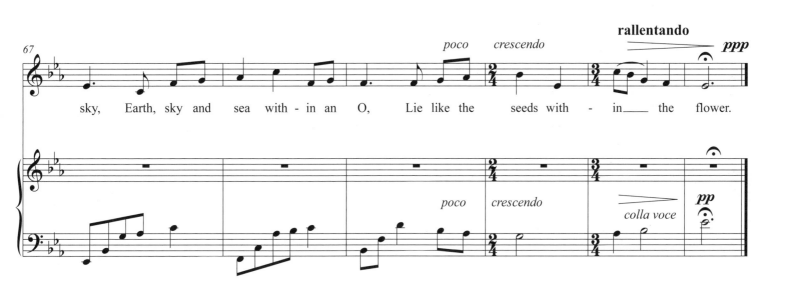

sky, Earth, sky and sea with - in an O, Lie like the seeds with - in the flower.

poco crescendo   **rallentando**

poco crescendo   *colla voce*

There was a naughty boy

Words by
JOHN KEATS

Music by
PAUL AYRES

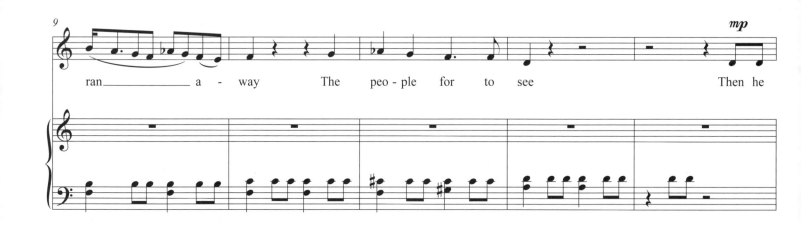

for Caroline

If there are angels

Words by
CAROLINE NATZLER

Music by
CECILIA McDOWALL

Gently flowing ♩ = 106

mp sempre legatissimo

Con Ped.

mp dolce

p dolce

If there are an - gels I hope,_____ I

hope__ their wings, tri - an - gu - lar, ex - act_____ and lift - ing

p

mp

94

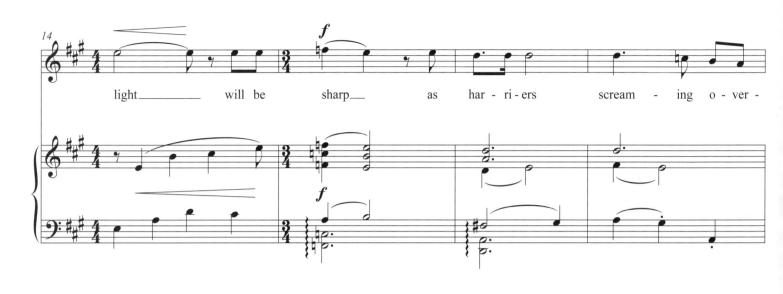

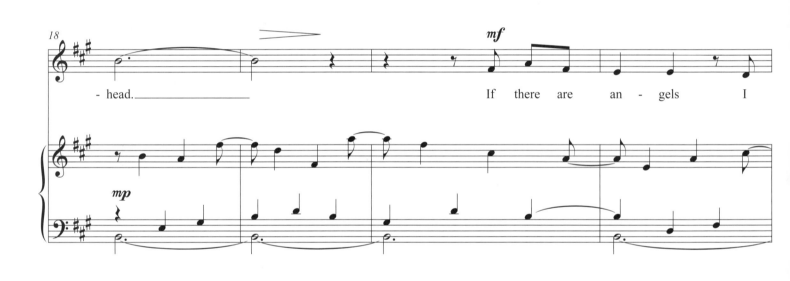

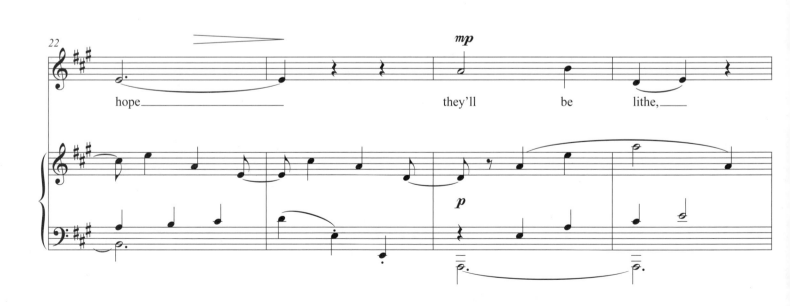

mus - cu - lar_____ pranc - ing and danc - ing in the air, mock -

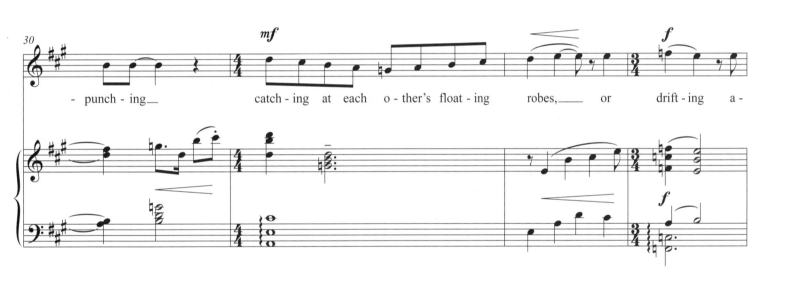

- punch - ing___ catch - ing at each o - ther's float - ing robes,___ or drift - ing a -

- way a - lone, robes_____ draugh - ty,_____ or curl - ing

into silence. I hope, I hope they'll be in - ward

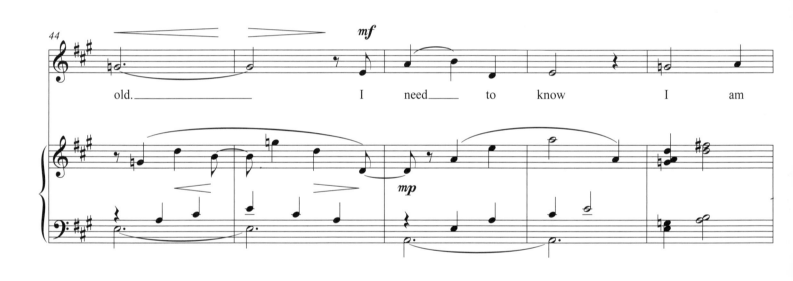

old. I need to know I am

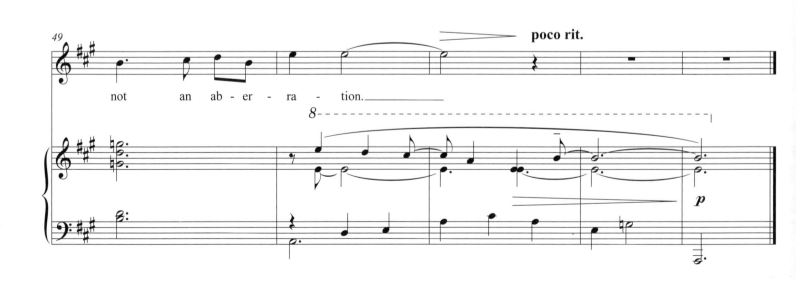

not an ab - er - ra - tion.

Performance notes

Liza Lehmann (1862–1918): **The swing** from Twelve Songs of Childhood – The Daisy Chain (page 1)
Words: Robert Louis Stevenson (1850–94)
Early in her singing career, Liza Lehmann spent some time studying the songs of Schumann with his widow, Clara, gaining a thorough knowledge of his many song cycles. It has been said that the song cycle in England was firmly set in motion by her. 'The swing' is one of *Twelve Songs of Childhood – The Daisy Chain*, with most of the texts coming from Robert Louis Stevenson's, *A Child's Garden of Verses*. Benjamin Britten was said to be very fond of the songs. The $\frac{6}{8}$ time gives a strong lilt to the music; big, arpeggiated chords in the piano introduction set the scene and are then used at specific points to maintain the feeling of movement; the vocal line sails up and down with octave leaps and broken chords, the *portamenti* giving a wonderful sense of 'whoosh through the air'! Careful attention should be given to the musical detail of the final 'joyously humming' section – accents, *diminuendo*, *poco rall*, the pause and *a tempo*, all contributing to the happy satisfaction of the child at the end of the ride.

Ralph Vaughan Williams (1872–1958): **The sky above the roof** (page 4)
English words: Mabel Dearmer (1872–1915)
In 1908, Vaughan Williams set words by Paul Verlaine (1844–96), translated from the French by Mabel Dearmer. Verlaine was imprisoned for two years for shooting and wounding another French poet, Arthur Rimbaud, during a violent quarrel. Perhaps the words of this poem express Verlaine's regret and anger for lost and wasted time. A still calm is called for at the start – a sense of resignation that life is going on outside the prison cell and the poet cannot be a part of it. A seamless line, with breaths avoided in mid-phrase, will help in evoking the atmosphere. A slower pace is needed from, 'Ah God! A life is here', and the piano postlude slows again, so it is important to keep things flowing at the start of the song. Dynamic markings should be followed closely.

Roger Quilter (1877–1953): **O mistress mine** No. 2 from Three Shakespeare songs, op. 6 (page 6)
Words: William Shakespeare (1564–1616)
Quilter is a songwriter with a unique and instantly recognisable style, his songs displaying his melodic gift and use of rich harmonies, his literary taste and his sensitivity to the accentuation of the words. He composed many settings of Shakespeare, beginning in 1905 with three that include this beautiful love song, the text coming from Act II, Scene 3 of *Twelfth Night*. The song has a light and graceful quality, demanding sensitive gradation of tone and a degree of rhythmic flexibility from the performers.

arr. **Herbert Hughes** (1882–1937): **She moved thro' the fair** Traditional air from County Donegal (page 9)
Words adapted from an old ballad by Padraic Colum (1881–1972)
Born in Belfast, Hughes was one of several significant contributors to the folksong movement that flourished in the early 20th century. Not only the music of Ireland but also its poets inspired him, especially W B Yeats and Padraic Colum. Hughes's beautiful setting of the latter's poem, adapted from an old ballad, hauntingly evokes the plaintive nature of the words. Imaginative colouring of the vocal tone will help in the characterisation of the first person narrator and his lost love. Care is needed in learning the rhythmic patterns; it is important to feel the dotted minim pulse strongly, whether in $\frac{6}{4}$ or $\frac{9}{4}$ so that the *con moto* element of the tempo indication is fulfilled and the melody can have a natural, easy flow, especially in the final section with its threes against twos. ['won't slight you for your lack of kind' = won't fail in courtesy or respect because you are not of noble birth or wealthy]

Ralph Vaughan Williams: Linden Lea (page 13)
Words: William Barnes (1801–86)
Although Vaughan Williams wrote songs and partsongs in the 1890s, the earliest composition that is widely known is *Linden Lea* which was written in 1901. This setting of words by William Barnes, a Dorset dialect poet, is subtitled, 'A Dorset Song' but it is not, of course, a traditional folksong. There is a fresh, open-air quality about it at the start; spring turns to autumn and the fruit ripens; those that work and make their money in the town are pitied; the poet doesn't have to worry about an irritable boss; no-one will see him frowning as he is a free man and able to be out of doors or to go home to where his apple tree waits for him. A simple flow is required, with some rhythmic flexibility and dynamic colour. A breath should be avoided in the phrase 'the apple tree do lean down low in Linden Lea', to preserve the sense of the words. The extra energy at the start of the third verse is followed by firm purpose for 'I be free to go abroad' before the ending settles quietly and contentedly.

Frank Bridge (1879–1941): **E'en as a lovely flower** (page 17)
Words: Kate Kroeker (1845–1904) after Heinrich Heine
Frank Bridge made a reputation as an outstanding conductor and chamber music player, and his compositions show poetic insight, highly professional craftsmanship and essential Englishness. Britten became his only composition pupil at the age of eleven. This song, written in 1903, has, perhaps, something of the drawing-room ballad about it but it is no less beautiful and elegant for that. The long *legato* lines need to be sung with gentle tenderness of expression, sweetness of tone and sensitive dynamic shading. The words might be interpreted as being sung by a man to his lover or, perhaps, by a mother to her young child.

John Ireland (1879–1962): **Spring sorrow** (page 21)
Words: Rupert Brooke (1887–1915)
Ireland reacted positively to the poets of his own time and *Spring sorrow* is arguably his most complete miniature. The line is exquisitely shaped to match the emotions of the poem and both conveying much more than appears on the surface. It is springtime; the hawthorn buds appear; my heart, frozen all winter, thaws and puts out its own buds but they are full of sad memories. A *legato* line is required throughout; with an appreciation by the singer of Ireland's carefully chosen note values for the word setting. The piano part has gently moving harmonies, almost as if designed for a string chamber group, and there are a few carefully placed chromatics, which highlight and colour the emotions. ('frore' = frozen)

John Ireland: I have twelve oxen (page 23)
Words: Early English
Four colourful herds of oxen are described grazing in different places in this simple, strophic song, which has something of the folksong about it. The piano accompaniment is chordal but with the four colours suggested by different rhythmic arrangements, accidentals and articulation for each stanza, with a holding back of the tempo for the start of the fourth, and a quick finish. The vocal line has simple rhythms and an extended final phrase, which includes a slightly lengthened top F. This enjoyable and lively song would make an excellent end to a group of songs for a recital.

Michael Head (1900–76): **The ships of Arcady** No. 1 from Over the Rim of the Moon (page 28)
Words: Francis Ledwidge (1891–1917)
Michael Head is known almost exclusively for his vocal compositions and was famous for his one-man recitals of his own music. This song has a marvellously dreamlike quality and should not be performed too slowly, so that a floating momentum can be achieved throughout complete phrases. Follow the composer's detailed phrasing and expression marks closely and enjoy creating the misty atmosphere.

Frederick Keel (1871–1954): **Trade winds** No. 2 from Three Salt-Water Ballads (page 33)
Words: John Masefield (1878–1967)
A smoothly flowing rhythm is called for and discretion needs to be used about breathing places in order to preserve the musical phrases and the sense of the words. Enjoy painting Masefield's words with a good variety of tonal colour; the piano accompaniment helps in this with its rich, rolling bass notes in verses 1 and 2, the *staccato* articulation and high chords for the 'squeaking fiddle' and the lighter texture and pp for the night-time of verse 3. ['soughing' = murmuring, rushing or rustling sound (of wind)]

Herbert Howells (1892–1983): **The widow bird** No. 3 from Four Songs, op. 22 (page 36)
Words: Percy Bysshe Shelley (1792–1822)
Teaching, examining, adjudicating and 'making people sing' played a big part in Howells's life as well as composing. This calmly expressive and very effective setting of Shelley's poem has a piano accompaniment that portrays the ceaselessly turning millwheel. While other composers have used the turning of the millwheel to suggest life and energy, 'The widow bird' is sad, wintry and cold, with no prospect of a thaw to cheer the spirit of the bird. The dynamics form an arch from pp up to mf and down to ppp, and both piano and voice need to flow seamlessly. A totally still stance and 'invisible breathing' will help in evoking the atmosphere.

Rebecca Clarke (1886–1979): **Infant Joy** (page 39)
Words: William Blake (1757–1827)
Rebecca Clarke, principally known as a viola player, was one of the most important British women composers in the first half of the 20th century and her choice of texts for her songs reveals her considerable literary taste. In her setting of Blake's 'Infant Joy' (*Songs of Innocence*, 1789) she portrays a whole range of emotion in a touching and perfect miniature. This is an imagined dialogue between a two-day old baby and its parent. Subtle changes of tonal colour and expression will help to evoke the conversation but the song is to be performed 'very simply and not too slowly', presumably to avoid sentimentality. Changes of metre, tempo and dynamic should be carefully noted. The vocal line is *legato*, apart from in bar 11, where the voice should approximate to speech. Poise is needed for the very soft entry on 'sweet' in bar 13. The piano accompaniment is beautifully written so that it too joins in the conversation with imitation and comment.

Elizabeth Poston (1905–87): **Sweet Suffolk owl** (page 41)
Words: Thomas Vautor (Songs of Divers Airs and Natures, 1619)
Elizabeth Poston distinguished herself in a wide field of musical activities; as a collector of folksong; as a member of the BBC music staff; as a writer of scores for radio productions and films, including *Howards End* (1970), and as an editor of folksong, carol and hymn collections. *Sweet Suffolk owl* was one of seven songs published when she emerged as a composer at the age of 20. It shows her personal style of writing, which stemmed from the neo-classical tradition. The song is beautifully crafted, with clean lines and a flowing melody demanding vocal ease and flexibility from the singer through the frequent melismas, which conjure up the calls of the owl. The crotchet pulse must be felt strongly so that the rhythmic patterns can be clearly pointed. At the same time, rhythmic flexibility is called for, so the composer's directions should be followed closely, especially from bar 30: faster, lightly and playfully for the mouse (bars 30–31); slightly slower than the original speed for the dirge (bars 32–35); and an indication for the singer to use discretion as to the timing and expression of the cadenza-like descending phrase (bars 37–39). ['trimly dight' = neatly dressed]

Benjamin Britten (1913–76): **The birds** (page 45)
Words: Hilaire Belloc (1870–1953)
Written in June 1929, when Britten was 15 years old, and revised in 1934, *The birds* was dedicated to his mother who was an amateur singer. Britten chose to set a poem of Belloc who was born and brought up a Roman Catholic and showed in almost everything he wrote, an ardent profession of his faith. The song grows in intensity from a gentle beginning and then dies away to a solemn and peaceful ending. The composer gives very clear directions as to the expression for both singer and accompanist.

arr. Herbert Hughes: A young maid stood in her father's garden (page 48)
Words: Traditional Irish
Here is a touching story that requires imaginative contrasts of vocal tone to portray the narrator, the sailor and the young maid. The melody flows smoothly, with written out ornaments, and although the rhythms are simple, care needs to be taken as they vary subtly to match the words.

Michael Head: Mamble (page 52)
Words: John Drinkwater (1882–1937)
This wonderfully leisurely song is a setting of words by John Drinkwater, from his *Collected Poems* (1923). Mamble is a small village on the A456 to the northwest of Worcester lying, as the poem says, to the north of the River Teme. The 'walking' piano accompaniment and *cantabile* lines invoke a gentle amble in the countryside. The poet wonders what life and people are like in Mamble but decides not to go there in case the reality doesn't live up to his vision of the place. He chooses another road, as anywhere in Worcestershire is worth visiting when the fruit trees are in blossom! Michael Head's instinctive feeling for the words requires the singer to remain true to the written note values (rhythm) and expression marks; the composer's carefree 'tra-la-lah' suggests the singer walking away into the distance. ['lissom' = lithe, supple, agile]

Mátyás Seiber (1905–60): **O your eyes are dark and beautiful** No. 4 from Four Greek Folk Songs (page 56)
English words: Peter Carroll
Seiber, born in Budapest and a student of Kodály, settled in England in 1935, establishing himself as a freelance musician and much-respected teacher of composition. He met an untimely death in a car crash in the Kruger National Park in South Africa in 1960. Folk music from around the world was a recurring interest, many arrangements being published throughout his life including *Four Greek Folk Songs*, written in 1942. No. 4 is a charming song, full of vitality and passion. The vocal melody is simple but needs poise and control, especially for the articulation and the little *portamenti*. A gentle *p* and full-bodied, expressive *f* should be equally telling in the voice, and the pianist can enjoy the fiery outbursts of the interludes with a twinkle in the eye.

Ned Rorem (b. 1923): Two songs (**Little elegy** & **On a singing girl**) (pages 60 & 67)
Words: Elinor Wylie (1885–1928)
Ned Rorem, the American composer, diarist and essayist, was brought up in Chicago and studied in New York, also spending several years in Paris and Morocco. His initial concentration was on writing solo songs and early on, *Time* magazine called him 'the world's best composer of art songs'. It has been said that he was able to breathe notes into words while leaving the thoughts of a poet intact. Rorem's settings of Wylie's sad poems, *On a singing girl* and *Little elegy* were composed in 1946 and 1948 and the music marvellously captures and colours their moods. Both should be performed with a calm elegance, poise and sweetness of tone.

Michael Rose (b. 1926): **See, see, mine own sweet jewel** (page 62)
Words: Anon. ?16th century
Michael Rose's main musical activities have been in writing and broadcasting, but he studied composition with Bernard Stevens in the 1950s and has written a number of songs and choral pieces at intervals all through his life. *See, see, mine own sweet jewel* was one of the earlier songs and is a real gem, speaking volumes in just twelve short bars. It should be sung very simply, bringing out the shy approach of the young lover, the tender pride with which he offers his gift and the sudden burst of desperation with which the song ends. The chordal writing in the piano part is warmed with beautiful colour at the mention of the robin redbreast and starling, and the singer should take care to place the intonation very precisely at this change to Db major. The final phrase should be left hanging uncertainly in the air.

Aaron Copland (1900–90): **Long time ago** No. 3 from Old American Songs – First Set (page 63)
Words: Ballad, adapted by George Pope Morris, from the Harris Collection of American Poetry and Plays in Brown University.
Copland's settings of *Old American Songs* exhibit his love of the humble side of American life – of banjo and fiddle tunes, early minstrel melodies, folk-hymns, children's songs and ballads, and their style of performance. *Long time ago*, a ballad first appearing in 1837, is given a sympathetic treatment. The voice part and piano accompaniment weave in and out of each other continuously, and the singer must be rhythmically precise and entirely confident in maintaining independence of line, so that a secure ensemble can be achieved. (By substituting 'his' for 'my' in the penultimate phrase, the song can be made as appropriate for performance by a female singer as a male.)

Aaron Copland: Little horses No. 1 from Old American Songs – Second Set (page 69)
Words: Lullaby
Little horses is a children's lullaby song originated in the Southern States. Copland sets the words with touching understanding – first the slow, somewhat dragging tempo for the parent singing softly and soothingly to the baby and then the faster pace when a coach and horses are promised if only the child will go to sleep! Rhythmic precision is demanded from the performers here: some dryness in the accompaniment and crisp diction from the singer. The final section should be sung very gently, with smiling tenderness of expression.

Michael Rose: The lark in the clear air (page 73)
Words: Sir Samuel Ferguson (1810–86)
This setting of a traditional Irish melody is all the more beautiful for its clarity and simplicity. After a gently musing opening, warm, harp-like chords in the accompaniment support the feeling of growing anticipation of the imminent declaration of love. Out of this, the single line song of the skylark rises inspirationally in the accompaniment (bars 27–30) before the arpeggiated chords return. Don't sing this song too slowly – the metronome marking is ♩ = 76 – and avoid sentimentality; think of calmness and happiness on a cool sunny day in the country. (In order to suit the performer, 'he' could replace 'she' in bars 15 and 23, and 'him' could replace 'her' in bar 19.)

Howard Ferguson (1908–99): **The apron of flowers** No.1 from Five Irish Folksongs (page 75)
Words: Irish folksong
Howard Ferguson's output of compositions, beginning in 1927 and ending in 1959, was modest, but each work made a decisive impression. Later, he turned to the editing of keyboard music and enjoyed an equally successful career as a piano recitalist and teacher of composition. Here, he takes a simple and lovely folksong and provides an ornamented accompaniment in which the grace notes, played before the beat, contribute to the folksong style and add an almost sobbing, sighing quality to the music. The mood is hypnotic and bittersweet. I loved a young man; he transferred his affections to another; now I must search for a special flower to ease my heart and mind. The song is slow and quiet, apart from some short phrases in the piano part, which sing out of the texture at the *mf* level.

Robert Dray (1917–88): **In praise of ale** (page 79)
Words: Anon. 16th century
Robert Dray, known by the nickname of 'Dick', read music and French at Trinity College and King's College, London. He became a schoolmaster and taught modern languages but was also active as an organist, pianist and composer. Two of his attractive output of songs are included in this album. 'In praise of ale', written in 1979 and dedicated to my husband, Christopher, who was a former pupil and colleague, is a splendidly boisterous and rousing drinking song. A metronome marking of ♩ = 104 seems about right. Put plenty of life into the words but observe the dynamic markings so that the climaxes are really telling.

Robert Dray: The Virgin's cradle hymn (page 83)
Words copied from an old print by Samuel Taylor Coleridge (1772–1834)
The Latin words of this song were copied by Coleridge from a print in a German village and given the title *The Virgin's cradle hymn*: 'Sleep Jesus; your mother is smiling when she sees such a sweet sleep. If you don't sleep your mother weeps and prays while singing as she spins. Come, sleep sweetly, little sweeting.' Robert Dray's beautiful setting needs a relaxed 2-in-a-bar feeling (♪ = c.96). Some rhythmic flexibility is called for, as well as a change of vocal colour for the middle section. The ending should be *estinto* – as soft as possible.

Christopher Field (b. 1940): **Spell of creation** (page 85)
Words: Kathleen Raine (1908–2003)
Christopher Field, a graduate of Trinity College, Cambridge and the Royal Academy of Music, has combined a career as a schoolmaster with that of a freelance musician. As a singer and choral conductor he has always found inspiration in the texts he has been called on to interpret, and when writing for voices, an important aspect of his musical life, the music inherent in a text has frequently provided inspiration for his composition. The music and magical words of this song develop in complexity as the poet throws shafts of light onto the mystery of creation, enabling us to catch glimpses of the truth. Opening with the simplicity of the unaccompanied description of the growth of a seed into a tree, together they move on to the wonders of human love and the awe-inspiring, life-giving properties of the sun, before coming full circle back to the distilled simplicity of the opening. Sing this with a vision of the elements of creation always in your mind's eye – see the sky reflected in the sea and the brilliance of the bird of gold – and adapt the vocal colour to suit the words.

Paul Ayres (b. 1970): **There was a naughty boy** (page 90)
Words: John Keats (1795–1821) from a letter to his sister, Fanny Keats
Paul Ayres is a freelance musician, working as a composer, arranger, conductor, organist and accompanist. He has written many solo songs as well as choral and theatre works. He told me that he chose these words because he liked their simultaneous combination of seriousness and light-heartedness. They are a nice way of saying 'the grass is greener on the other side'. The drone effects and Scotch snap rhythms are happy little national references and the song trips along with vitality at the two-in-a-bar metronome marking. Bar 9 will need careful, slow practice to ensure precision of notes and rhythm. All the sustained notes should be full-length and the final phrase should be left hanging in the air wonderingly. As with all song preparation, it is wise to read through the text before approaching the music, particularly here, where the lines of the poem are very short and the composer has chosen to add emphasis and verbal humour by repetition.

Cecilia McDowell (b. 1951): **If there are angels** (page 93)
Words: Caroline Natzler (b. 1950) from the poem This Side of Paradise
Cecilia McDowell has a wide experience in performing, teaching and composing. She has, in her own words, 'a close tenderness to writing for voices, which can be highly dramatic and expressive in so many ways.' She chose to set words from *This Side of Paradise* for this song book because she says, 'I enjoy the evocative imagery and the mood of hopefulness in the poem. The angels suggest many things to me; brightness and lightness, a vibrant playfulness, an ethereality and a deep wisdom.' Of the song, she told me that it should be performed with a 'floating fluidity and a dignified innocence'. She intends the changes of time signature to 'unbuckle the words and give them freedom', and the syncopation in the piano accompaniment to provide buoyancy of support when the singer has sustained notes. The voice should be lightly floated off the final note. When I asked her about the phrase, 'I need to know I am not an aberration', Cecilia said that she felt it was to do with seeking affirmation that we are part of the scheme of things, that there is a purpose to it all and that Caroline had put her idea rather delightfully – that she hoped to be in accordance with things metaphysical.